From Rote to Note

9 PIANO PIECES

Elementary Piano Pieces That Reinforce Theory and Technique
Designed to be Taught without Traditional Notation

E. L. Lancaster *and* Kevin Olson

Contents

© 2022 by the Frances Clark Center

Piano Education Press

The Frances Clark Center

90 Main Street, P.O. Box 651

Kingston, NJ 08528

ISBN-13: 978-1-7377237-1-4

About This Book

From Rote to Note contains nine pieces that reinforce keyboard theory and technique. Each ce is based on a theoretical or technical concept that students encounter at beginning levels of st/ and is designed to be taught from a musical map without the aid of traditional notation. Once st/nts can play from the abstract representation, they can examine the notated score. They move inte/tually from rote to note, experiencing musical elements before relating them to notation.

The book is geared toward students of varying age groups and can easily be adapted in/existing curriculums. It is especially useful for students who play other instruments and are famil/with rhythm notation. Students who are not familiar with rhythm notation can learn the rhythms by e/after hearing teacher demonstrations.

Each piece includes the following:

- An abstract that maps the piece to aid with memory and practice at home

- Traditional notation of the piece, sometimes with an optional duet accompan/ent

- A teacher section that identifies the piece's concept, gives steps for introdu/g the musical map, and outlines strategies for teaching the piece by rote

About Rote Teaching

Rote teaching can be defined as a student imitating a teacher or a recording of music with minimal reference to a musical score. It has several benefits for students and can even aid in securing note-reading skills if integrated into a solid curriculum that combines rote- and note-based learning. It forms the basis of developing literate, independent musicians. Some advantages of rote teaching follow:

Artistry: Students can apply listening skills to focus on artistically bringing out musical character.

Creative Exploration: Students can improvise on the rote materials, using their own musical ideas to further explore the concept.

Ear Training: Students learn to listen more intently to identify concepts.

Memory: Students begin to memorize the music from the first introduction to the pieces.

Motivation: Students are motivated by rote instruction since they can often play more difficult music than they can read.

Musical Understanding: Students can explore theoretical concepts such as phrase structure and form.

Pattern Recognition: Students learn to identify patterns visually from the abstract representation and aurally from hearing the music.

Sound to Symbol: Students can fully experience musical ideas before encountering the symbols for these concepts.

Technical Development: Students can focus on the technical aspects of playing without having to be concerned with reading notation.

Rock Steady

Use RH finger 3 throughout on black keys only. Repeat using LH finger 3 throughout.

D = Down   U = Up

E. L. Lancaster & Kevin Olson

With energy!

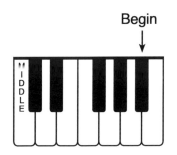

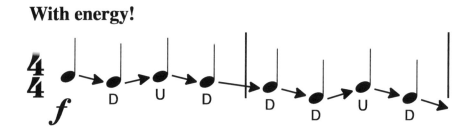

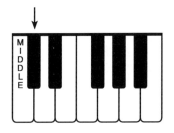

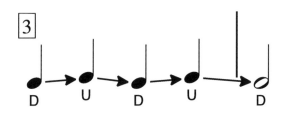

Move back to starting note.

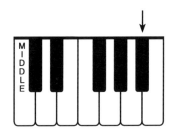

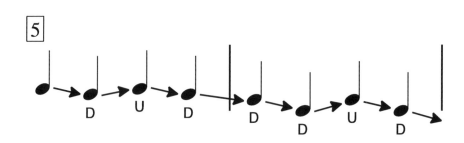

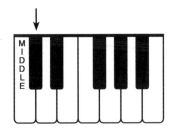

Rock Steady

E. L. Lancaster & Kevin Olson

Optional Duet Accompaniment

TEACHER

Rock Steady (Moving Up and Down on Black Keys)

Introduce and Explain Map

1. Play only black keys with RH finger 3.
2. An arrow points to the starting key for each line.
3. The rhythm is notated.
4. The direction to move is shown by arrows, D for down and U for up.

Demonstrate and Teach by Rote

1. Play line 1 of the map while saying "begin, down, up…"
2. Play line 2 of the map while saying "begin, up, down…"
3. Play lines 1 and 2 of the map while saying "begin, down, up…"
4. Repeat steps 1–3 for lines 3 and 4.
5. Play the entire piece and add optional duet accompaniment.

Black 'n' Blue

Use RH finger 3 throughout on black keys only.

D = Down   U = Up   S = Same

E. L. Lancaster & Kevin Olson

Moderately fast

Move back to starting note.

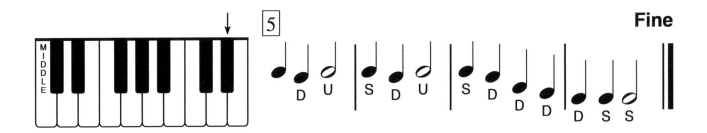

Fine

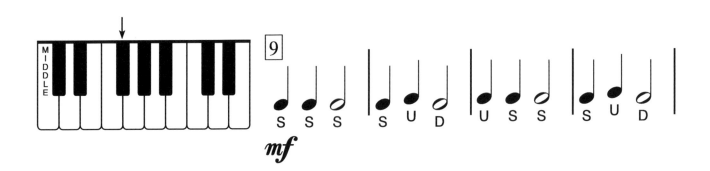

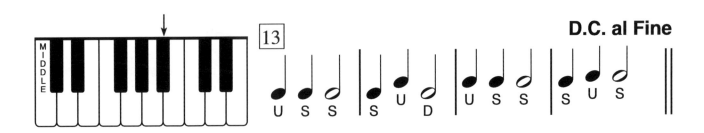

Black 'n' Blue

E. L. Lancaster & Kevin Olson

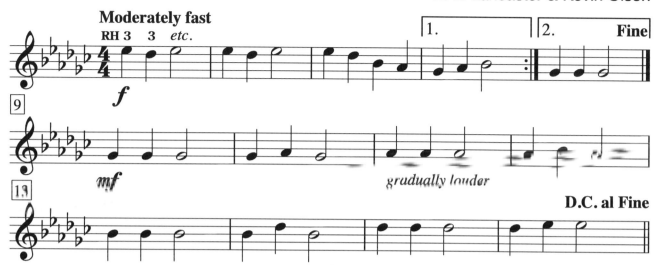

Optional Duet Accompaniment

TEACHER

Black & Blue (Moving Up, Moving Down, and Repeating Black Keys)

Introduce and Explain Map

1. Play only black keys with RH finger 3.
2. An arrow points to the starting key for each line.
3. The rhythm is notated.
4. The direction to move is shown by arrows, D for down, U for up, and S for same.

Demonstrate and Teach by Rote

1. Play line 1 while saying "begin, down, up, same…"
2. Play line 2 while saying "begin, down, up, same…"
3. Play lines 1 and 2 while saying "begin, down, up, same…"
4. Repeat steps 1–3 for lines 3 and 4.
5. Explain how the first two lines will be repeated after the *D.C. al Fine* measure.
6. Play the entire piece and add optional duet accompaniment.

Stargazing

Depress the damper (right) pedal throughout.

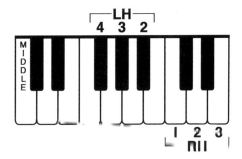

E. L. Lancaster & Kevin Olson

Mysteriously

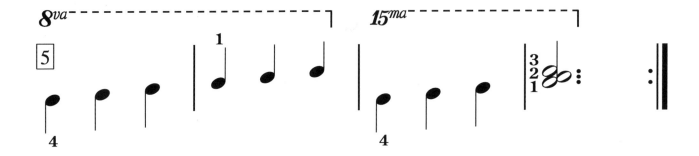

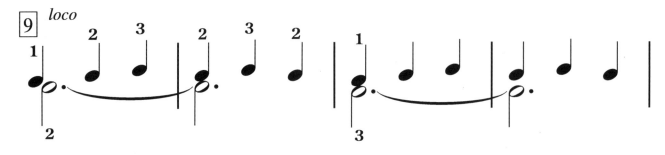

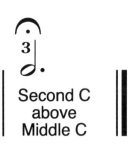

Stargazing

E. L. Lancaster & Kevin Olson

TEACHER

Stargazing (Whole Steps)

Introduce and Explain Map

1. The entire piece uses only whole steps—black keys for the LH (except for middle C in m. 16) and white keys for the RH.

2. The keyboard at the beginning shows the starting position for mm. 1 and 9. The position moves up an octave in mm. 5 and 7.

3. The LH moves to middle C in m. 16, and the RH moves to the second C above middle C in m. 17.

4. The rhythm is notated.

Demonstrate and Teach by Rote

1. Play line 1 while saying finger numbers.

2. Play line 2 while saying finger numbers. Point out octave moves.

3. Play lines 1 and 2 while saying finger numbers. Point out octave moves.

4. Play the first notes in both hands in mm. 9, 11, and 13.

5. Play mm. 9–14 hands together.

6. Play mm. 15–17 noting how the hands move.

7. Play the entire piece.

Five-Finger Waltz

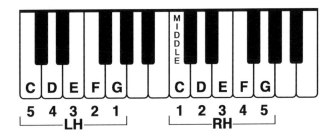

E. L. Lancaster & Kevin Olson

Moderate waltz tempo

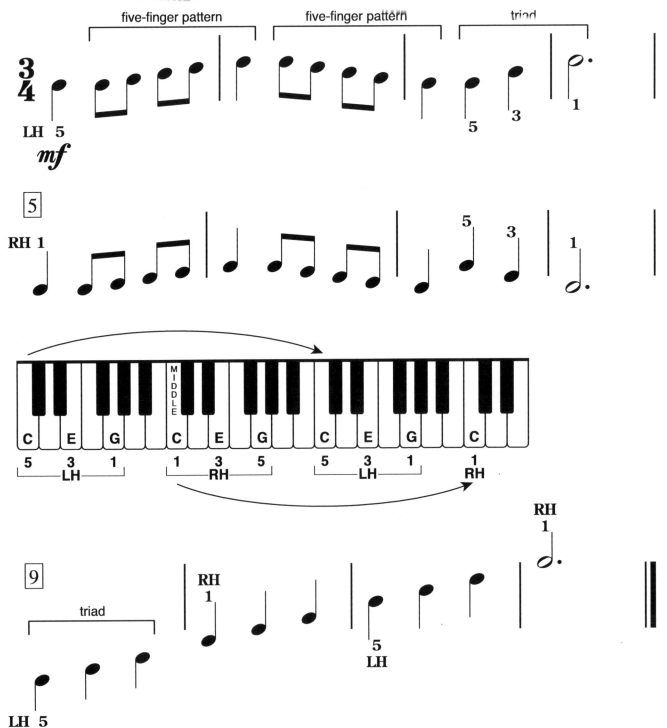

Five-Finger Waltz

Moderate waltz tempo

E. L. Lancaster & Kevin Olson

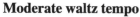

Optional Duet Accompaniment (Student plays one octave higher than written.)

Moderate waltz tempo

TEACHER

Five-Finger Waltz (Major Five-Finger Patterns and Triads)

Introduce and Explain Map

1. Point out ascending and descending five-finger patterns and the ascending LH triad in mm. 1–4.

2. Point out ascending and descending five-finger patterns and the descending RH triad in mm. 5–8.

3. Point out hand-over-hand triads in mm. 9–12.

Demonstrate and Teach by Rote

1. Play the LH five-finger patterns and triad in mm. 1–4.

2. Play the RH five-finger patterns and triad in mm. 5–8.

3. Play the hand-over-hand triads in mm. 9–12.

4. Play the entire piece and add optional duet accompaniment.

5. Repeat steps 1–3 in the keys of F and A-flat.

6. Play the piece with the optional duet accompaniment in the keys of F and A-flat. (See page 22.)

Tipping the Scales

In both hands, use finger 3 throughout.

E. L. Lancaster & Kevin Olson

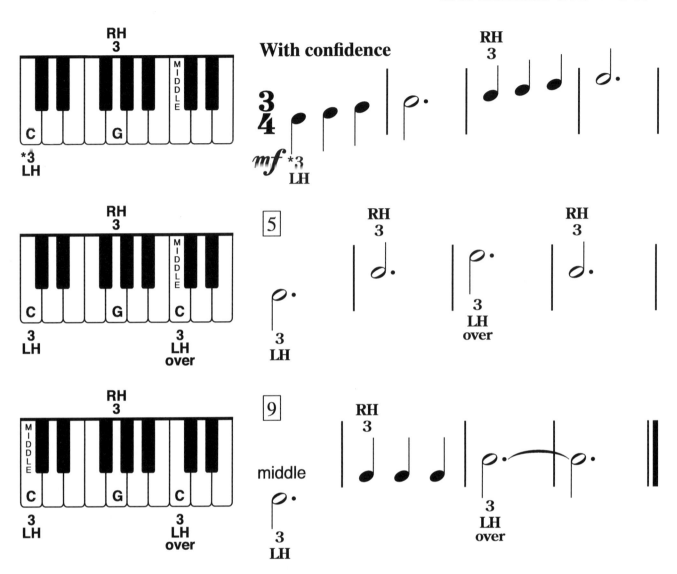

*Optional fingering for line 1: LH 4 3 2 1; RH 1 2 3 4

Optional Duet Accompaniment (Student plays one octave higher than written.)

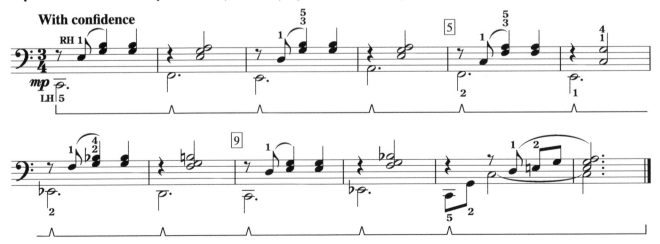

Tipping the Scales

E. L. Lancaster & Kevin Olson

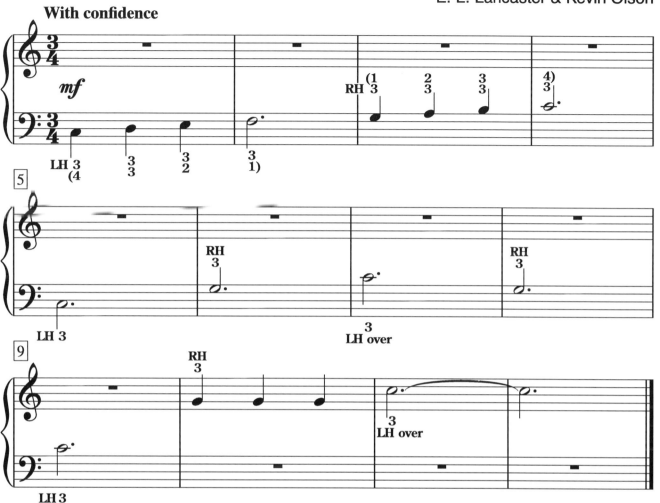

TEACHER

Tipping the Scales (Major Scales, Tonic and Dominant Tones)

Introduce and Explain Map

1. Line 1 plays an ascending major scale using only finger 3. The first four notes are played with the LH; the last four notes are played with the RH.

2. For a legato sound, use the optional fingering.

3. Lines 2 and 3 alternate tonic and dominant tones with the LH crossing over the RH for mm. 7 and 11.

Demonstrate and Teach by Rote

1. Play the major scale using finger 3 of the LH for the first four notes and finger 3 of the RH for the last four notes.

2. Play tonic and dominant tones in mm. 5–8 with the LH starting on the C below middle C and then crossing over the RH for m. 7.

3. Play tonic and dominant tones in mm. 9–12 with the LH starting on middle C and crossing over the RH for m. 11.

4. Play the entire piece and add optional duet accompaniment.

5. Repeat steps 1–3 in the keys of F, G, and D major.

6. Play the piece with the optional duet accompaniment in the keys of F, G, and D major. (See page 23.)

Major to Minor

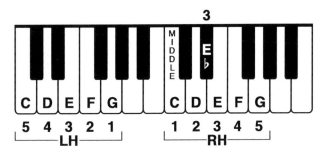

RH 3 plays both E and E♭.

E. L. Lancaster & Kevin Olson

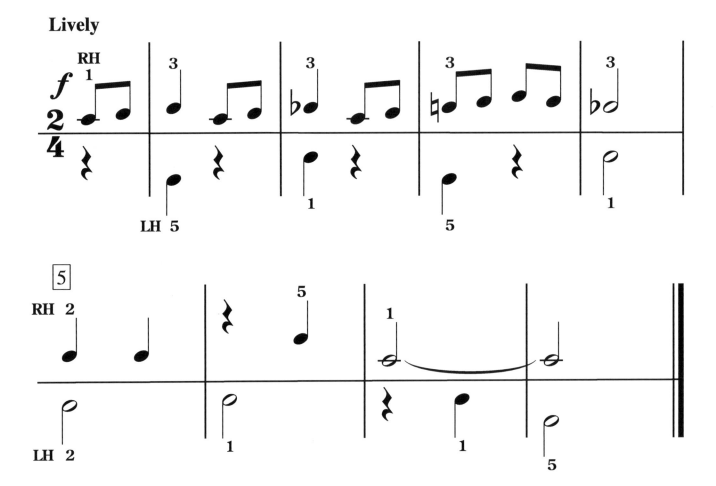

Optional Duet Accompaniment (Student plays one octave higher than written.)

Major to Minor

E. L. Lancaster & Kevin Olson

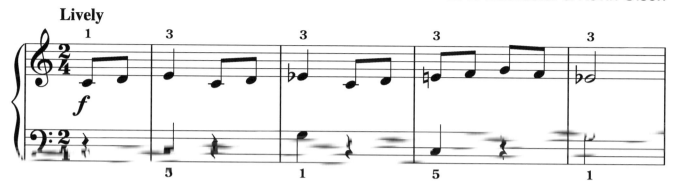

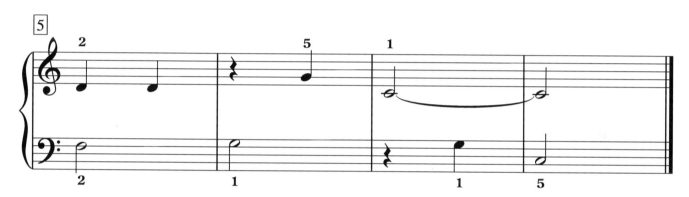

TEACHER

Major to Minor (Major and Minor 3rds, Hands-Together Coordination)

Introduce and Explain Map

1. Notes above the line are played with the RH; notes below the line are played with the LH.

2. RH finger 3 plays both E and E♭.

Demonstrate and Teach by Rote

1. Play the RH of mm. 1–4 pointing out where E changes to E♭.

2. Play the RH of mm. 5–8 identifying the intervals between the notes.

3. Play the entire RH.

4. Play the LH identifying the intervals between the notes.

5. Play the hands-together notes in mm. 1–5.

6. Play mm. 6–8 pointing out how the hands alternate.

7. Play the entire piece and add optional duet accompaniment.

8. Play the piece with the optional duet accompaniment in the keys of G, D, F, and B-flat major. (See page 24.)

Five Alive Rock

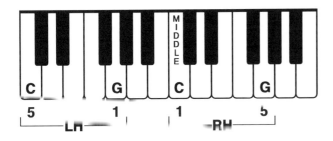

E. L. Lancaster & Kevin Olson

Five Alive Rock

E. L. Lancaster & Kevin Olson

TEACHER

Five Alive Rock (Intervals of 3rds, 4ths, and 5ths)

Introduce and Explain Map

1. Pitches above the line are played with the RH; pitches below the line are played with the LH.

2. Numbers indicate the interval above or below the letter name.

3. A circle indicates a half note (mm. 2, 4, 6, 8, 12); arrows indicate a whole note (m. 12); all other notes are quarter notes.

Demonstrate and Teach by Rote

1. Play the LH harmonic intervals in mm. 1–2, 5–6, and 9–10. Find other measures that are similar.

2. Play all the RH intervals. Determine which intervals are harmonic and which intervals are melodic.

3. One at a time, play each line hands together.

4. Play the entire piece.

Five-Six-Seven-Eight

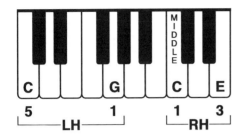

C. L. Lancaster & Kevin Olson

Moderate rock tempo

Five-Six-Seven-Eight

E. L. Lancaster & Kevin Olson

Moderate rock tempo

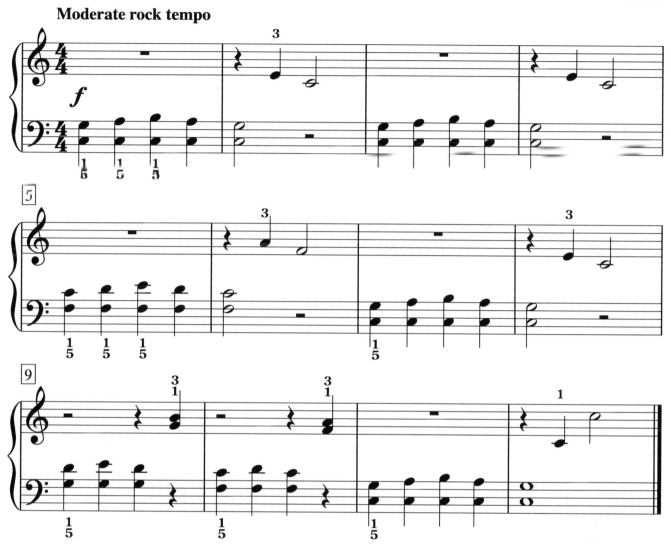

TEACHER

Five-Six-Seven-Eight (Intervals of 5ths, 6ths, 7ths, and octaves)

Introduce and Explain Map

1. Pitches above the line are played with the RH; pitches below the line are played with the LH.

2. Numbers indicate the interval above or below the letter name.

3. A circle indicates a half note (mm. 2, 4, 6, 8, 12); arrows indicate a whole note (m. 12); all other notes are quarter notes.

Demonstrate and Teach by Rote

1. Play the LH harmonic intervals in mm. 1–2, 5–6, and 9–10. Find other measures that are similar.

2. Play all the RH intervals. Determine which intervals are harmonic and which intervals are melodic.

3. One at a time, play each line hands together.

4. Play the entire piece.

Midnight Chase

RH plays all white-key chords and a few single notes. LH plays broken fifths and a few single notes.

Play all chords and single notes staccato.

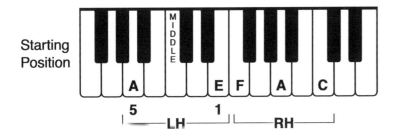

E. L. Lancaster & Kevin Olson

Moderate rock tempo

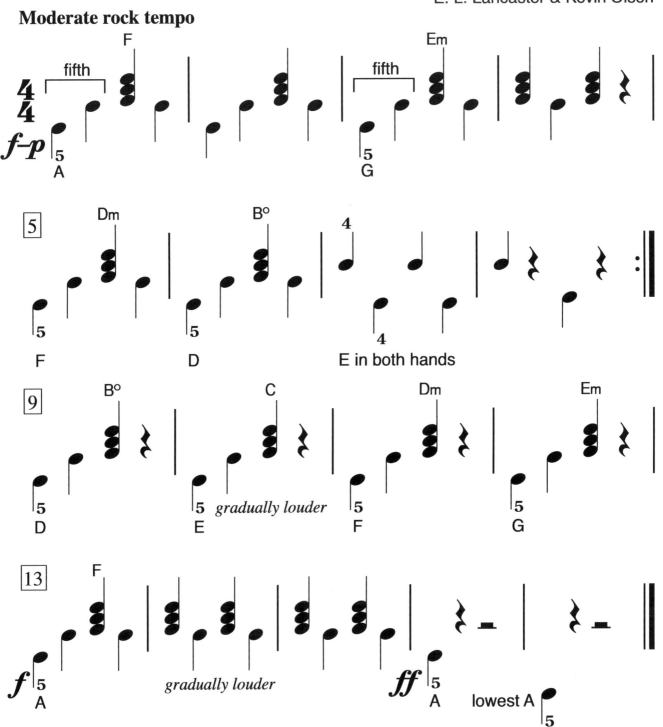

Midnight Chase*

E. L. Lancaster & Kevin Olson

Moderate rock tempo

*Teacher: See page 22 for instructions.

TEACHER

Midnight Chase (Chords Built on White Keys, Interval of a 5th)

Introduce and Explain Map

1. The RH plays chords labeled above the notation. In mm. 7–8, it plays single notes.

2. The LH plays a single note on beat 1 and a fifth above that note on other beats. In mm. 7–8 and 16–17, it plays only single notes.

3. All chords and single notes are played staccato.

Demonstrate and Teach by Rote

1. Play the RH white-key chords for the entire piece.

2. Play the LH given notes and fifth above for the entire piece.

3. Block the RH chords and LH fifths hands together for the entire piece. Notice that the thumbs are always on adjacent white keys.

4. First, play mm. 1–6 and 13–15.

5. Then, play mm. 9–12.

6. Play the single notes in mm. 7–8 and 16–17.

7. Play the entire piece.

OPTIONAL DUET ACCOMPANIMENTS

Five-Finger Waltz (pages 10–11)

Key of F Major (Student plays one octave higher than written.)

Key of A♭ Major (Student plays one octave higher than written.)

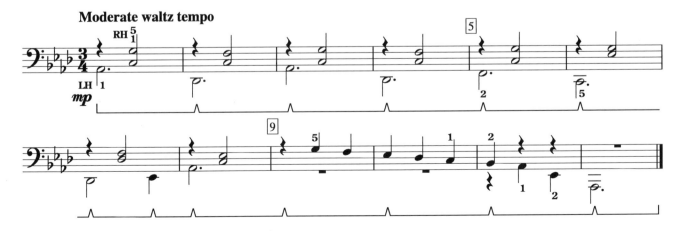

Tipping the Scales (pages 12–13)

Key of F Major (Student plays one octave higher than written.)

Key of G Major (Student plays one octave higher than written.)

Key of D Major (Student plays one octave higher than written.)

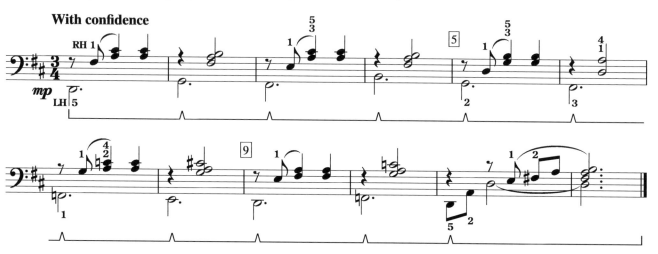

Major to Minor (pages 14–15)

Key of G Major (Student plays one octave higher than written.)

Key of D Major (Student plays one octave higher than written.)

Key of F Major (Student plays one octave higher than written.)

Key of B♭ Major (Student plays one octave higher than written.)

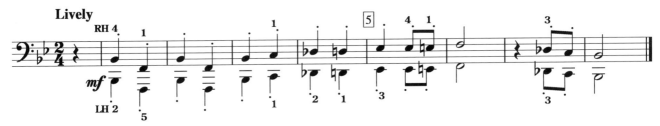

Made in the USA
Middletown, DE
28 February 2023

25875696R00015